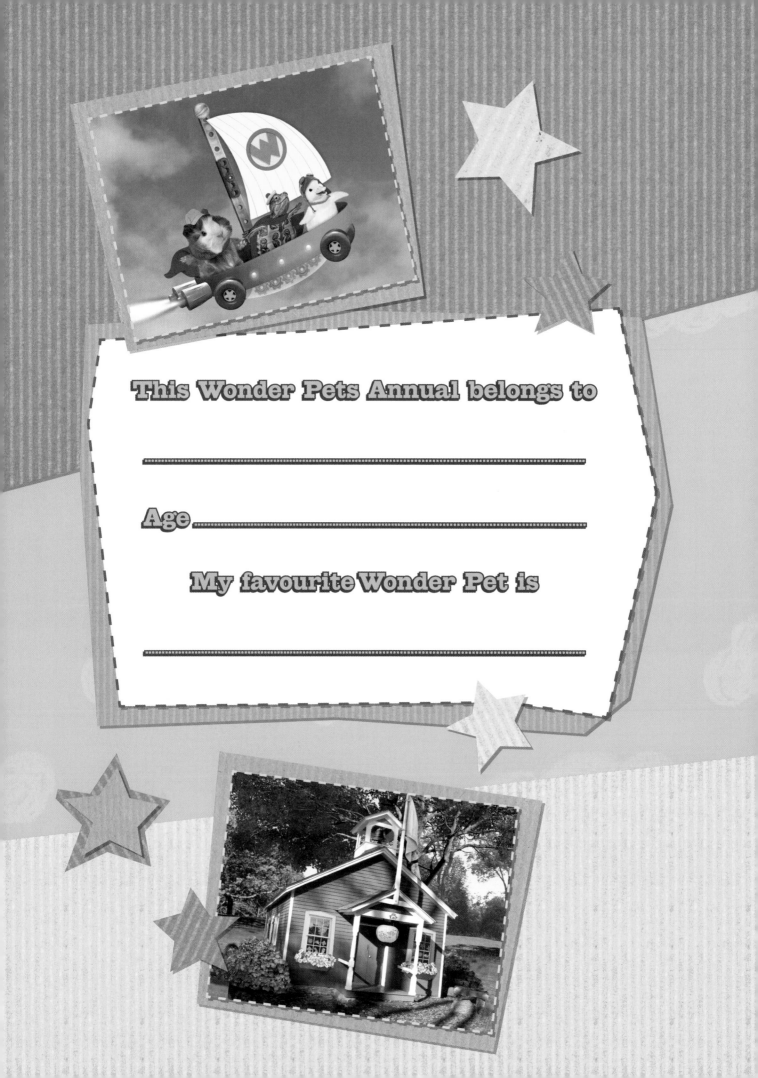

This Wonder Pets Annual belongs to

....

Age ....

My favourite Wonder Pet is

....

Annual 2011

EGMONT
We bring stories to life

First published in Great Britain 2010
by Egmont UK Limited,
239 Kensington High Street, London W8 6SA
Text by Pippa Shaw. Design by Jo Bestall

ISBN 978 1 4052 5320 8
1 3 5 7 9 10 8 6 4 2
Printed in Italy

Note to parents: Adult supervision is required when sharp-pointed items, such as scissors, are in use.

What's inside:

"Hello, I'm Ming Ming."

"Hello, I'm Tuck."

"Hello, I'm Linny."

We're the Wonder Pets!

Can you find 10 big pieces of celery like this one on the pages of this annual?

Meet the Wonder Pets!

The Wonder Pets all live together in this classroom. They are class pets by day, but when there's an animal in trouble somewhere, they spring into action!

Linny

Linny is a guinea pig. Her house is a cage filled with cosy sawdust. She is very clever and knows a lot about the places the Wonder Pets travel to and the animals they meet.

8

Tuck

Tuck is a turtle. He's a really good swimmer, so his tank has fresh, cool water for him to splash around in. Tuck always gives his friends hugs when they need cheering up.

Ming Ming

Ming Ming is a yellow duckling. She uses her fluffy wings to fly, and she speaks bird, which is handy when the Wonder Pets are out on their adventures! Ming Ming loves to take part and will try anything.

The Wonder Pets Save the Panda

At the end of a long day at school,
the Wonder Pets heard a familiar noise.

"The phone! The phone is ringing!"
they sang as they scampered to answer it.

"It's a baby panda, stuck in a tree." said Linny as
she answered it. "And she has a poorly tummy, too."

The Wonder Pets went to build the flyboat, but the wheels were too high for them to reach.

"I'll go up the ladder and pass them down," said Linny as she climbed up high.

What's the highest thing you can see where you are?

Tuck and Ming Ming helped Linny to lower the wheels to the ground.

Soon, the flyboat was built and the Wonder Pets were ready to go!

The Wonder Pets flew all the way to China. They even saw the Great Wall!

Linny landed the flyboat, and together the Wonder Pets followed the cries of the baby panda until they found her high up a bamboo shoot.

Tuck had an idea. "We can fly the flyboat up to save the baby panda."

What words rhyme with fly?

So the Wonder Pets climbed back into the flyboat.

But when Linny tried to steer it to the baby panda, they couldn't get through. There was just too much bamboo in the way.

They landed again with a bump!

13

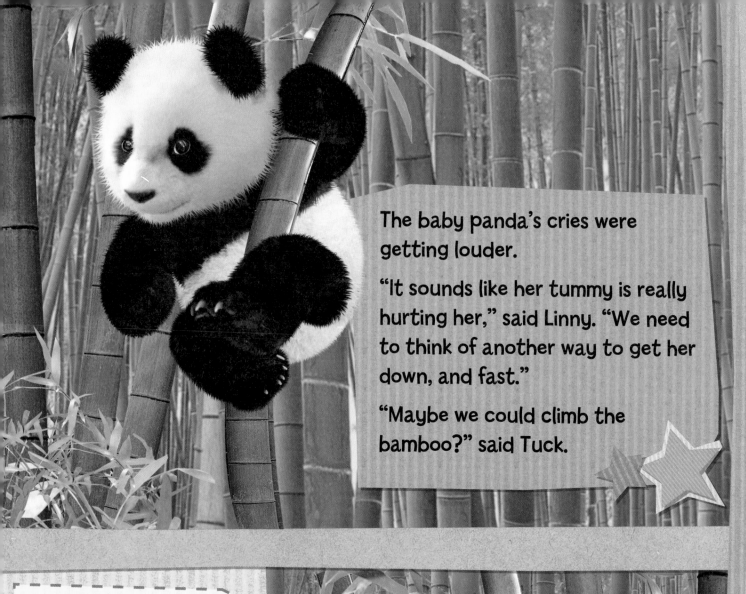

The baby panda's cries were getting louder.

"It sounds like her tummy is really hurting her," said Linny. "We need to think of another way to get her down, and fast."

"Maybe we could climb the bamboo?" said Tuck.

But the bark was too slippery, and Linny, Tuck and Ming Ming couldn't grip on properly.

"I wish we could climb the bamboo like it was a ladder," said Tuck.

"We'll make a ladder from bamboo to climb up to the panda," said Linny, and the three friends began to build the ladder.

♪ "What's going to work?"
"Teamwork!"
"What's going to work?"
"Teamwork!"

Rub your tummy, to show the panda how to feel better.

Soon, the ladder was ready. The Wonder Pets climbed up to the top and took the baby panda by the paw.

"We are the Wonder Pets, and we're here to help you!" they told her as they all climbed down together.

What colours are the mummy and baby pandas?

The baby panda ran to her mummy, who had been very worried!

"This calls for some celery!" said Linny as she pulled some from her cape. The panda's mummy gave them soy sauce to sprinkle on it. It was delicious!

Their work was done, and it was time to go home. **Go Wonder Pets, yay!**

Shadowy Shapes

Which of these shadows matches Ming Ming? Circle the one you think is right.

1

2

3

4

Which animals do the other shadows belong to?

Spot the Difference

These two pictures of the Wonder Pets in the flyboat may look the same, but there are 5 differences in picture b. Colour in a star for each difference you find!

1
2
3
4
5

19

Answers on page 68.

Colour Linny

Colour in this picture of Linny to get her ready for action!

Write Linny's name by tracing the dotted lines with a pencil or pen.

Linny

Hat Match

Before the Wonder Pets leave the school house, they all put on hats and capes. Draw lines to match them to their correct hats.

1

a

2

b

3

c

The Wonder Pets Save the Sea Turtle

School time was over and all the children had gone home. Just then, the phone began to ring.

"The phone! The phone is ringing!" Linny, Tuck and Ming Ming sang together.

When they answered the phone, they heard a strange noise.

"It's a baby sea turtle in Japan!" Linny gasped. "She can't find the sea!"

Lie on your tummy and use your arms and legs to pull yourself forwards like a turtle.

Soon the Wonder Pets and the flyboat were ready to go and save the baby sea turtle.

"Erm, Linny?" Ming Ming said. "May I steer the Flyboat today?"

"Sure thing!" Linny smiled to her friend.

But there was a problem ...

23

What is your favourite toy?

"I can't see the cubby hole to fly out of," said Ming Ming.

"Don't worry, Ming Ming," Linny told her. "Tuck and I will help!"

So Linny and Tuck built a path from toys shaped like sushi to show Ming Ming the way, and soon they were flying to the rescue!

Ming Ming gently landed the flyboat on soft white sand.

The Wonder Pets quickly found the baby sea turtle, as she was the only little turtle who was crawling away from the ocean!

"We are the Wonder Pets and we're here to help you!" they told her.

25

"It's getting dark, Wonder Pets," said Linny. "We must think of something fast!"

"I know," piped up Tuck. "Why don't we make a path to the ocean for her, like we did for Ming Ming when she couldn't find the cubby hole?"

What could the Wonder Pets use to build the path?

So the Wonder Pets gathered
shiny shells to make a path ...

♪ "What's going to work?"
"Teamwork!" ♪ "What's going to work?"
♪ "Teamwork!" ♫

... and they finished it just before it got dark.

The seashell path glinted and twinkled
in the moonlight as the baby sea turtle
slowly started to crawl along it.
The Wonder Pets stood by, cheering her on.

With a little splash, the baby sea turtle landed in the ocean. The Wonder Pets had done it!

"This calls for some special Japanese celery!" said Linny, as she pulled three sticks of celery from her cape. Soon, it was time to fly home again.

Go Wonder Pets, yay!

Count the three sticks of celery in the picture.

29

All About Sea Turtles

The Wonder Pets saved the sea turtle! Hooray!
Now find out more about these amazing creatures.

Sea turtles can live to be over 80 years old.

They come to the surface to breathe air and can hold their breath underwater for up to three hours.

Although they spend most of their lives in water, sea turtles lay their eggs on sandy beaches. When the baby turtles hatch, they dig themselves out of the sand and crawl to the ocean.

You can find sea turtles in almost every ocean around the world, except for the Arctic Ocean. It's far too cold for them.

Colour Tuck

Tuck is a turtle, too! Colour him in as neatly as you can.

Write Tuck's name by tracing the dotted lines with a pencil or pen.

Tuck

Under the Sea

Sea turtles aren't the only creatures that live under water. Look for the animals in the big picture below. When you've found them, tick the box next to them.

Can you think of any other animals that live in the sea?

whale   **seahorse** 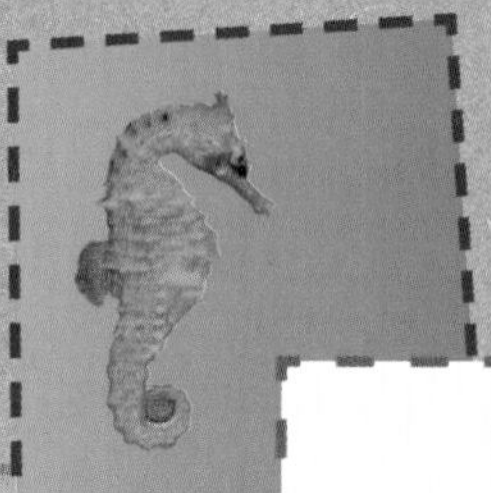   **fish**    **sea turtle**    **dolphin**

Make a Match

Find the little picture of Linny that matches the big one here.
Do you know what she is dressed up as in each of her outfits?

a

b

d

e

c

f

33

The Wonder Pets Save the Elephant

School was over for another day. Today, the children had learnt about Kenya.

The phone began to ring. It was a baby elephant with his trunk stuck in the mud.

"We have to help him!" said Tuck.

The Wonder Pets got ready to go.

Put your arm in front of your nose and wave it around like an elephant's trunk.

But the flyboat was stuck under a beanbag.

"I know!" Linny said. "We'll build a seesaw. When the seesaw comes down, the beanbag will go up and we'll be able to move the flyboat."

So the Wonder Pets made a seesaw, and soon the flyboat was free! They all hopped in and flew out of the cubby hole.

The Wonder Pets were soon flying over Kenya. They saw heavy hippos and stripy zebras below.

Before long, the Wonder Pets had found the baby elephant. He was very worried about his trunk being stuck in the mud.

"If only there was something we could grab on to to pull him out," said Linny.

What could the Wonder Pets use to pull the baby elephant out?

"We could pull his tail," said Linny.

So the three Wonder Pets pulled and pushed and heaved and hoed. But the baby elephant didn't budge.

Tuck had a different idea. "When the flyboat was stuck, we got it out with a seesaw!"

But their seesaw was back in the classroom! They had to build a new one. Ming Ming found a rock for the base, and Tuck found a log to go across the top. Now all they needed was something really heavy to make it go down.

Point to something heavy where you are.

38

The Wonder Pets went to find the heavy hippo they had seen earlier. But he was too busy eating grapes to help them. So clever Ming Ming carried the grapes over to the seesaw!

"What's going to work?"
"Teamwork!"

"What's going to work?"
"Teamwork!"

As soon as the hippo stood on the seesaw, the baby elephant squelched out of the mud. He was free! Tuck rushed over to give him a hug.

The Wonder Pets had saved the baby elephant, with some help from a heavy hippo! They celebrated with some celery, and then jumped back in the flyboat. It was time to go home.

Go Wonder Pets, yay!

Can you think of a time when you helped someone?

Beautiful Butterfly

The Wonder Pets love beautiful butterflies. Make your own to hang wherever you like by following these simple steps.

You will need:
- coloured cardboard
- safety scissors
- a bin bag, cut in half
- coloured tissue paper
- PVA glue and brush
- sticky tape
- string

1 Lay your bin bag on a flat surface. Tear shapes and strips from your coloured tissue paper.

2 Stick your tissue paper pieces together on the bin bag using your PVA glue. You'll need to cover an area big enough to cut two wings from. When you have finished, leave it to dry.

3 While your tissue paper is drying, ask an adult to help you cut a sausage shape from the coloured cardboard. This will be the body of your butterfly.

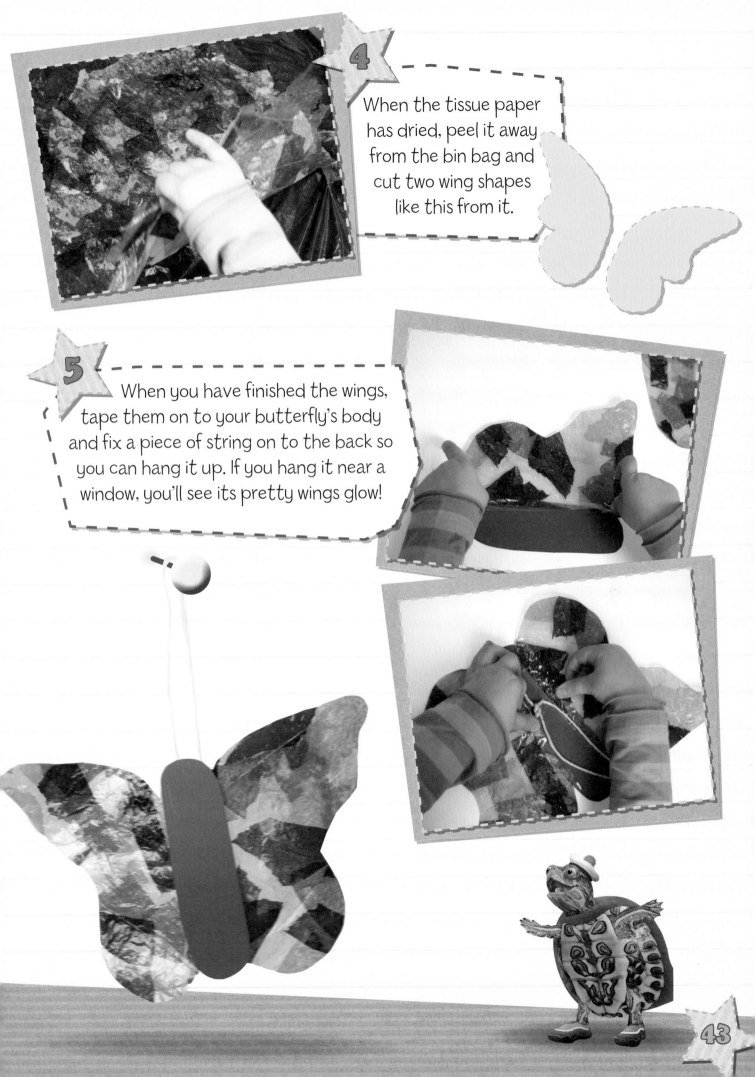

4

When the tissue paper has dried, peel it away from the bin bag and cut two wing shapes like this from it.

5

When you have finished the wings, tape them on to your butterfly's body and fix a piece of string on to the back so you can hang it up. If you hang it near a window, you'll see its pretty wings glow!

43

Colour Ming Ming

Ming Ming is a very fluffy little duckling!
Colour her in using your best crayons.

Write Ming Ming's name by tracing the dotted lines with a pencil.

Ming Ming

Animal Chatter

Different animals make different noises. Match the animals below with the noises they make.

1

2

3

4

5

a **woof**

b **squawk**

c **baa**

d **miaow**

e **moo**

Answers on page 68.

The Wonder Pets Save the Kitten

 Wonder Pets    flyboat   Tuck

 kitten   Linny   Ming Ming

It was the end of another day at school. The  were all in their homes when the phone began to ring. "The phone! The phone is ringing!" they sang together.

It was a who had fallen into

a canal in Venice. She was very scared.

"Let's save the kitten," the

sang. They tried to build the

 , but the mast was too far

away for to reach. Clever

made a bridge out of a ruler to

reach the mast. She passed it to

and . The  were

ready to go! As they were flying,

spotted the  in the water,

holding on to some driftwood.

The  landed and got into

a boat to save the . But the

 was too far away for the

 to reach.  had an

idea. "Let's make a bridge to reach the

. The  worked

together to make a bridge from the

boat's oars.

Soon the  was safe and sound.

 ,  and  had saved

the kitten. It was time to eat some

celery to celebrate!

Go Wonder Pets, yay!

Celery Maze

All the Wonder Pets love to eat **celery**. Can you guide them through the maze to their favourite snack?

Start

Finish

Favourite Food

Now the Wonder Pets have their celery, draw **your favourite food** in the space below. It could be anything you like!

The Phone is Ringing!

When there's an animal in trouble somewhere, it calls the Wonder Pe on their special phone! Learn how to make your own Wonder Pets phone below.

1 Ask an adult to help you poke a hole in the bottom of each yogurt pot.

You will need:
- 2 clean, empty yogurt pots
- string
- red paper
- safety scissors
- sticky tape
- gluestick and pencil

2 Thread the string through the bottom of each yogurt pot. Tie a knot in the string to hold it in place. If your first knot isn't big enough, tie it again to make it bigger.

52

3 Cut 2 strips of red paper which are as wide as the base of the yogurt pots. Wrap one around each of the pots and stick it in place with some tape.

4 Copy or cut out the two Wonder Pets symbols below and glue one to the side of each pot. Your phone is now ready!

5 To use your phone, ask a friend to take one yogurt pot and move away as far as the string will allow. Speak into your end, and if your friend holds theirs to their ear, they should be able to hear you!

Make a ringing noise like a phone!

WONDER PETS!

WONDER PETS!

Someone's in Trouble!

The Wonder Pets are flying off to help another animal in trouble somewhere. Who do you think it might be?

Flyboat Maze

The Wonder Pets need to save a baby kangaroo before it gets dark! The sun has already begun to set. Find the way through the maze for them, quick!

Start

Finish

The Wonder Pets Save the Reindeer

It was Christmas Eve and the Wonder Pets were about to open one present each when suddenly ...

"The phone! The phone is ringing!" they sang together as they hurried to answer it.

"It's one of Santa's baby reindeers!" gasped Linny. "She's stuck on thin ice at the North Pole!"

The Wonder Pets wrapped up nice and warm for their journey. Now all they had to do was build the flyboat. But one of the wheels was in the fish tank! How would they get it out?

Look for something the Wonder Pets could use to get the wheel out of the tank.

"Use the net!" said Ming Ming.

Together, the Wonder Pets fished the wheel out of the tank and put it on their festive flyboat.

"We're coming to save you Santa's baby weindeer!" cried Ming Ming, who was still holding her present as they flew out of the cubby hole.

The Wonder Pets were soon flying over the snowy ground of the North Pole.

As they flew on, they saw Santa's sleigh, loaded with presents. It looked heavy. Without the baby reindeer, the sleigh wouldn't be able to fly !

How many snowflakes can you see?

Linny landed the flyboat on the crisp snow. As they looked around, the Wonder Pets spotted the reindeer standing on a frozen pond. She looked scared, because the ice she was standing on was slowly cracking!

"I know what to do!" said Tuck.
"Ming Ming, open your present."

"OK," said Ming Ming happily.
She loved presents!

It was a purple jumper!

"We can use this jumper as a net to pick her up," Tuck told them. "Just like with the wheel!"

"But what about my pwesent?" Ming Ming asked, sadly.

What colour is the top you are wearing today?

Tuck and Linny gave Ming Ming a hug.

"Christmas isn't about presents!" they told her. "It's about being together and helping others."

Ming Ming agreed: saving the baby reindeer was more important.

So the Wonder Pets climbed into the flyboat and zoomed into the air. Tuck lowered the home-made net, and scooped up the baby reindeer, just as the ice cracked!

The Wonder Pets took the baby reindeer back to Santa's house, where she was hitched up to the sleigh. The three friends watched as the magic sleigh flew into the night, and then it was time to go home.

Back at the schoolhouse, the Wonder Pets found presents from Santa under the tree. Tuck got a snowglobe. Linny got some celery. And Ming Ming got the most special gift of all - another purple jumper!

Merry Christmas, Wonder Pets! Yay!

Clap your hands to show the Wonder Pets how well they did!

Story Quiz

Can you remember what happened when the Wonder Pets saved the baby reindeer? Circle the right answers to these questions. You can look back at the story if you need help.

1 Where did the Wonder Pets fly to save the reindeer?

a Greece

b The North Pole

c India

2 What did Tuck get for Christmas?

a a snowglobe

b a jumper

c celery

3 What colour was Ming Ming's new jumper?

a red

b purple

c blue

Answers on page 68.

Animal Homes

Animals live in all kinds of places. Do you know where these animals live? Draw lines to match them to their homes. If you get stuck, you'll find clues in the stories and activities in this book.

Count the Penguins

How many **baby penguins** can you count in this polar picture? Write the answer in the box below.

Waddle like a penguin! Keep your arms by your sides and your legs as close together as possible when you walk.

Answers on page 68.

Goodbye!

"Well Wonder Pets, our work here is done," says Linny with a smile.

Help Linny, Tuck and Ming Ming find their way home. Draw lines to match them to their homes, and wave them all goodbye.

1

2

3

a

b

c

Answers on page 68.

Answers

Page 18
Shadow 2 matches Ming Ming.

Page 19

Page 21
1-b; 2-c; 3-a.

Page 33
Picture e matches the big picture of Linny.

Page 45
1-d; 2-c; 3-a; 4-e; 5-b.

Page 50

Page 55

Start

Finish

Page 64

1-b; 2-a; 3-b.

Page 65

1-d; 2-a; 3-c; 4-b.

Page 66

There are 10 penguins in the picture.

Celery count

The celery was hidden on pages 8, 18, 21, 31, 32, 33, 45, 46, 55 and 65.

Page 67

1-c; 2-b; 3-a.